Smarty Pants

by Joy Cowley

I am a smarty pants,
rum-tum-toe.
Here is a racing car.

See me go.

I am a smarty pants,
rum-tum-tie.
Here is an airplane.

See me fly.

I am
a smarty pants,
rum-tum-tay.
Here is a trumpet.

6

See me play.

I am a smarty pants,
rum-tum-tim.
Here is a swimming pool.

See me swim.

I am a smarty pants,
rum-tum-tee.
Here is a mountain.

See me ski.

I am a smarty pants,
rum-tum-ting.
Here is a jungle vine.
See me swing...

and swing...

I am a smarty pants,
rum-tum-tum.
See me fall down
on my thumb.